PUFFIN CANADA

HYENA IN PETTICOATS

WILLOW DAWSON is a cartoonist from Vancouver who now resides in Toronto. She's the creator of *Lila and Ecco's Do-It-Yourself Comics Club* (Kids Can Press) and illustrator of award-winning graphic novels *No Girls Allowed* (Kids Can Press) and *Violet Miranda: Girl Pirate* (Kiss Machine). She is currently working on *100 Mile House* (excerpts published by Top Shelf 2.0). Her books have been supported by the Toronto Arts Council, the Ontario Arts Council, and the Canada Council for the Arts. In her spare time, she teaches comics at libraries, public and private schools, for the Parkdale Street Writers, and at the University of Toronto.

Visit her website at www.willowdawson.com.

Hyena in Petticoats

The Story of Suffragette Nellie McClung

WILLOW DAWSON

PUFFIN
CANADA

PUFFIN CANADA

Published by the Penguin Group

Penguin Group (Canada), 90 Eglinton Avenue East, Suite 700, Toronto,
Ontario, Canada M4P 2Y3 (a division of Pearson Canada Inc.)

Penguin Group (USA) Inc., 375 Hudson Street, New York, New York 10014, U.S.A.
Penguin Books Ltd, 80 Strand, London WC2R 0RL, England
Penguin Ireland, 25 St Stephen's Green, Dublin 2, Ireland (a division of Penguin Books Ltd)
Penguin Group (Australia), 250 Camberwell Road, Camberwell, Victoria 3124, Australia
(a division of Pearson Australia Group Pty Ltd)
Penguin Books India Pvt Ltd, 11 Community Centre, Panchsheel Park,
New Delhi – 110 017, India
Penguin Group (NZ), 67 Apollo Drive, Rosedale, Auckland 0632, New Zealand
(a division of Pearson New Zealand Ltd)
Penguin Books (South Africa) (Pty) Ltd, 24 Sturdee Avenue, Rosebank,
Johannesburg 2196, South Africa

Penguin Books Ltd, Registered Offices: 80 Strand, London WC2R 0RL, England

First published 2011

1 2 3 4 5 6 7 8 9 10 (WEB)

Copyright © Willow Dawson, 2011

This narrative draws upon dialogue and descriptions from Nellie McClung's
autobiographies *Clearing in the West* (1935) and *The Stream Runs Fast* (1945).

ONTARIO ARTS COUNCIL
CONSEIL DES ARTS DE L'ONTARIO

Manufactured in Canada.

LIBRARY AND ARCHIVES CANADA CATALOGUING IN PUBLICATION

Dawson, Willow
Hyena in petticoats : the story of suffragette Nellie McClung : a graphic novel / by Willow Dawson.

Includes bibliographical references.
ISBN 978-0-14-317779-1

1. McClung, Nellie L., 1873–1951—Juvenile literature—Comic books, strips, etc.
2. Suffragists—Canada—Biography—Juvenile literature—Comic books, strips, etc. 3. Feminists—
Canada—Biography—Juvenile literature—Comic books, strips, etc. 4. Authors, Canadian
(English)—20th century—Biography—Juvenile literature—Comic books, strips, etc. 5. Women
politicians—Canada—Biography—Juvenile literature—Comic books, strips, etc. I. Title.

HQ1455.M3D39 2011   j305.42092   C2011-906161-9

Visit the Penguin Group (Canada) website at **www.penguin.ca**

Special and corporate bulk purchase rates available; please see
www.penguin.ca/corporatesales or call 1-800-810-3104, ext. 2477 or 2474

For all the girls!

But especially Emily, for always
cheering me to the finish line.

It is the writer's place to bring romance to people, to turn the commonplace into the adventurous and the amusing, to bring out the pathos in a situation ... Words are our tools and must be kept bright ... I refuse to be carried through the sewers of life just for the ride ... I write if I have something to say that will amuse, entertain, instruct, inform, comfort or guide the reader.

—Nellie McClung

Contents

Introduction   1

1: Milk and Honey   2

2: Into the Stream   19

3: Sowing Seeds   31

4: Hyena in Petticoats   37

5: Windy Nell   49

6: Calamity of War   57

7: The House Is on Fire   71

8: Five Famous "Persons"   79

9: Leaves and Lanterns   87

Afterword   92

Bibliography   94

Acknowledgments   95

OCTOBER 20, 1873.
Chapter 1: Milk and Honey
GARAFRAXA ROAD, JUST OUTSIDE OF CHATSWORTH, ONTARIO.
WAAAAAAAAAAAAAAAAAAAAA

Is Mother okay?

Yes.

You have a new baby sister, Willie.

Her name is Nellie Letitia Mooney.

She's very little.

It's not your fault she's a girl. It'll be okay. We have enough boys to help with the farm work.

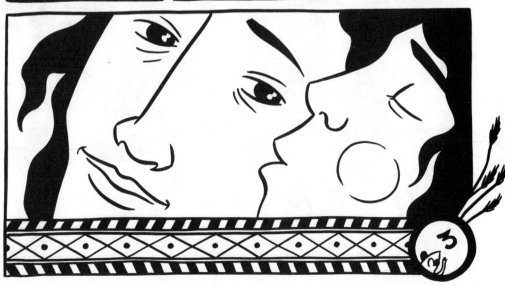

3

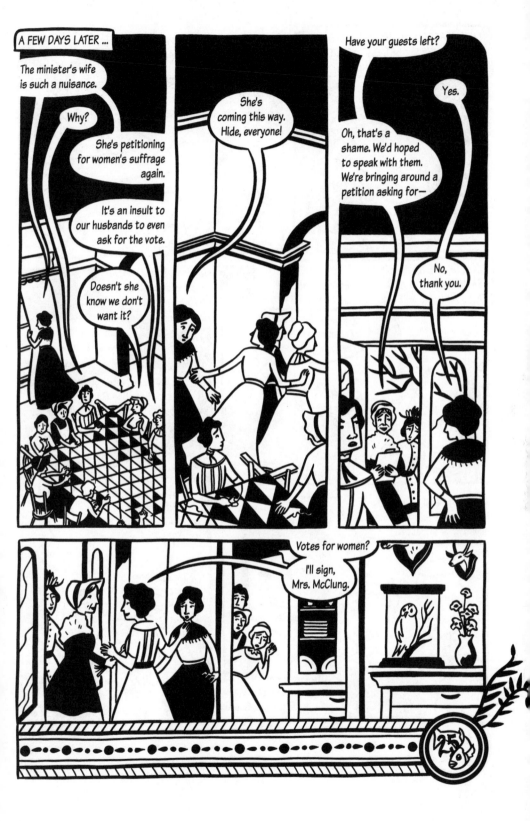

NELLIE UPGRADES HER TEACHING CERTIFICATE IN 1893 AND TAKES A POSITION IN TREHERN. SHE BOARDS WITH MR. AND MRS. MCCLUNG, WHO'VE JUST BEEN TRANSFERRED THERE, WHILE WES ATTENDS COLLEGE IN TORONTO. NELLIE AND WES EXCHANGE LETTERS FOR THE NEXT TWO YEARS.

Hmm. He wants to marry me.

Another letter from our son ... that's one each week! I think he's fond of you. We are too, Nellie.

I like Mrs. McClung a lot, and Wes is very good to me. I think we could have a good life together, but I'm still not sure I wish to marry. I never pictured myself as a wife

WES MCCLUNG AND HIS NEW BRIDE, MRS. NELLIE MCCLUNG, BOARD THE TRAIN BACK TO MANITOU.

Why do women have to suffer so much? They can't vote, they're not protected by the law, and yet they have to do all the work bearing and raising children. Women have endured too much and said nothing. Well, I'm not going to be meek and mild and resigned. Women should use their motherly ways to take care of the world. I've heard there's an organization called the Women's Christian Temperance Union that fights for women's rights. I'll join and help stir the deep waters of complacency.

DESPITE BEING BUSY RAISING A FAMILY AND RUNNING THE DRUGSTORE, NELLIE AND WES MAKE TIME FOR CONCERTS, READINGS, AND PLAYS.

That was incredible!

Some of you know me by my English name, E. Pauline Johnson, but I have another name, Tekahionwake.

My dear, your skin is very white and yet you say your father is an Indian. I would never have known it.

Is it true that you're of pure white blood?

Of course I am!

I would never have known it.

When she came out in her Mohawk clothes and performed that piece about her father's family, I was mesmerized.

Me too.

I wonder if she can meet with us before she leaves ...

TEKAHION TONITE

THE NEXT DAY ...

Were you proud when you first saw your verse in print?

Oh, yes. It's a huge feat for someone who's part Native.

Do you tour a lot?

Yes. I love performing and meeting wonderful people like you, but it can be exhausting.

Why do it, then?

I believe in the power of storytelling. A well-performed poem can make people see the world differently. It can bring joy and inspire hope.

34

NOVEMBER 1902.

Collier's has a short story contest. I think you should enter. We'll look after the house while you write.

I can't do it today, I have all these chores ...

Do you think E. Pauline would make such excuses? If you wait until you're ready, you'll never write.

THAT EVENING ...

How is it coming?

I've written two stories. I think I'm going to pick this one and send it in tomorrow after I edit it. Thanks for minding the children.

NELLIE DOESN'T WAIT TO HEAR FROM *COLLIER'S*. SHE BEGINS WRITING ARTICLES FOR THE LOCAL METHODIST SUNDAY SCHOOL PUBLICATIONS SOON AFTER SUBMITTING HER STORY.

SEVERAL MONTHS LATER ...

Dear Mrs. McClung,

Thank you for your submission to our contest. Sadly, your story did not win a prize. It's a bit too juvenile for our magazine but we really like your humour and originality.

Sincerely,
Collier's Weekly.

NELLIE REWORKS THE STORY INTO A NOVEL, *SOWING SEEDS IN DANNY*, AND SENDS IT OFF TO A DIFFERENT PUBLISHER.

What is this, Mrs. McClung? It's as heavy as a tree!

It's a story about an adventurous young girl named Pearlie Watson.

She sounds like you!

35

1911. WES IS EXPERIENCING TOO MUCH STRESS RUNNING THE DRUGSTORE, SO HE TAKES A JOB AT A LIFE INSURANCE COMPANY. THE COUPLE SELLS THE DRUGSTORE AND MOVES TO WINNIPEG, WHERE THEIR FIFTH CHILD, MARK, IS BORN.

Will you sign our petition? It's in favour of giving women the vote and allowing them to sit in Parliament.

Oh yes, absolutely!

I would like to sign as well.

What a fabulous performance!

Mrs. McClung, a few questions, please.

Are you worried what the Premier will think of your impersonation of him?

I hope he'll see the good humour in it. We certainly didn't mean any harm. We just wanted to make the point that women deserve the same rights as men.

THE PEL PUTS THE PLAY ON THREE TIMES. THEY RECEIVE MUCH ACCLAIM AND MAKE ENOUGH MONEY TO FINANCE THEIR ENTIRE CAMPAIGN.

WOMEN'S PARLIAMENT A HUGE SUCCESS!
JANUARY 29, 1914

Any doubt that women should be given the vote was erased last evening at the Walker Theatre. The Political Equality League put on a hilarious mock Parliament to a standing room only audience. "Windy Nellie" McClung played the part of the Premier while women of the PEL acted as the government and opposition. A group of men pleaded

DECEMBER 4, 1915. NELLIE RETURNS HOME FROM HER TOUR IN TIME TO SEE HER 18-YEAR-OLD SON, JACK, OFF TO WAR.

I really wish you wouldn't go. The trenches are no place for a boy, Jack.

You taught me to fight for what I believe in. I want to do something to help people, too.

67

DURING HER TIME IN PARLIAMENT, NELLIE CONTINUES TO ADVOCATE FOR THINGS LIKE BETTER WORKING CONDITIONS IN FACTORIES, MINIMUM WAGE, OLD AGE PENSIONS, MOTHERS' ALLOWANCES, AND PROHIBITION.

And finally, this Divorce Bill will enable women to leave with their children if it is proven to be in their benefit. Currently, men are the only ones with this privilege.

Thank you Mrs. Parlby. All those in favour say "aye."

TRUE TO HER NATURE, NELLIE DOESN'T ALWAYS FOLLOW THE RULES.

Aye

Aye

Nellie, you're not supposed to vote for the other side!

It doesn't matter which party forwarded it. If it's a progressive bill that will benefit women across the province, then I'll vote for it.

1923. WES IS TRANSFERRED AGAIN AND THE FAMILY MOVES TO CALGARY. NELLIE TRAVELS BACK AND FORTH BETWEEN CALGARY AND EDMONTON WHILE THE HOUSE OF COMMONS IS IN SESSION.

Aw. Why do you have to go again? You just got back.

I'm sorry, sweetie, but I have a great duty to fulfill for the people of this province. I'll be back next weekend.

DURING WEEKDAYS, NELLIE SPENDS HER SPARE TIME IN EDMONTON'S LIBRARY OF PARLIAMENT RESEARCHING HER NEXT NOVEL, *PAINTED FIRES*, SET IN PROGRESSIVE FINLAND.

75

BARS AND LIQUOR STORES HAVE RE-OPENED AS A RESULT OF ALBERTA'S LIQUOR CONTROL ACT. NELLIE IS FURIOUS!

Women buying liquor? But, how can that be?

LIQUOR SPECIAL 5¢ 5¢

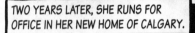

TWO YEARS LATER, SHE RUNS FOR OFFICE IN HER NEW HOME OF CALGARY.

The government is corrupt! It makes money off the very thing that destroys your precious families. Imagine your sons—and daughters—getting drunk every night instead of saving for their futures? Prohibition is the only way to stop the scourge of alcoholism ...

Who is this raging woman?

I don't know, but she's really intense.

1926

CALGARY ELECT

Ladies and gentlemen, the votes are in! George Webster is the Liberal winner!

FOR ALL HER PASSION AND HARD WORK, NELLIE LOSES TO ANOTHER CANDIDATE.

77

1929. NELLIE AND HER ALLIES, NOW CALLED THE FAMOUS FIVE, ASK PRIME MINISTER WILLIAM LYON MACKENZIE KING FOR HELP. HE PAYS FOR A LAWYER TO TRAVEL OVERSEAS AND REPRESENT THEIR CASE.

LONDON, ENGLAND, OCTOBER 18, 1929.

Excluding women from the Senate is uncivilized and old fashioned. The BNA Act was created specifically for Canada and is intended to live and breathe alongside a growing country.

The word "persons" in some of the clauses clearly refers to both men and women. We cannot understand why it should not be extended to the clause in question...

84

1930. CAIRINE WILSON BECOMES THE FIRST WOMAN APPOINTED TO THE CANADIAN SENATE. NELLIE IS DISAPPOINTED IT WASN'T HER WELL-DESERVING FRIEND EMILY MURPHY, BUT MEMBERS OF THE FAMOUS FIVE ARE STILL VERY HAPPY TO FINALLY SEE A WOMEN IN THE POSITION.

1932. WHEN NELLIE'S HEALTH BEGINS TO DECLINE, THE MCCLUNGS MOVE TO A FARM AT THE EDGE OF THE OCEAN IN VICTORIA, WHICH THEY NAME LANTERN LANE. WES RETIRES A YEAR LATER, IN 1933.

Chapter 9: Leaves and Lanterns

DESPITE HER BAD HEALTH, NELLIE STILL MANAGES TO RESPOND TO FAN MAIL ...

... WRITE REGULAR NEWSPAPER COLUMNS, WHICH SHE PUBLISHES IN *LEAVES FROM LANTERN LANE* (1936) AND *MORE LEAVES FROM LANTERN LANE* (1937), AND TWO AUTOBIOGRAPHIES.

1936. NELLIE BECOMES A MEMBER OF THE CBC BOARD OF GOVERNORS. SHE FEELS STRONGLY THAT RADIO HAS GREAT POTENTIAL FOR EDUCATION AND WOMEN'S PROGRAMMING.

NELLIE TOURS THE PROVINCE OF NOVA SCOTIA AS A SPEAKER ...

... AND THEN HEADS ACROSS THE OCEAN IN 1938 TO THE LEAGUE OF NATIONS IN GENEVA, WHERE SHE IS THE ONLY FEMALE DELEGATE.

Nellie McClung

91

Afterword

During her lifetime, Nellie McClung published sixteen books (several of which were and still are bestsellers), many articles in a variety of magazines and newspapers, and enjoyed a thriving political career. She toured Canada, the United States, and Europe extensively as a famous author and lecturer. Nellie had strong opinions against racism and would fight her entire life for the causes she believed in, including Prohibition, fair laws for women and immigrants, and fair labour laws. Many of her views were considered very radical in her time. One that remains controversial to this day was her belief in eugenics: the sterilizing of mentally handicapped children.

Nellie credited her rural upbringing on the plains of Manitoba as one of the main reasons for her success. She grew up on a farm in a pioneer village where women worked equally as hard as the men, resources were often scarce, and the entire town would pitch in to help with community projects or a neighbour in need. Nellie understood how difficult life was for most people. She understood their struggles, their passions, and the power that was possible when people were inspired to work together on a common goal. Though she lived most of her adult years in major cities, she generally preferred the country and its inhabitants.

Christianity was a huge part of Nellie's private and public life. She was born to a Scottish Presbyterian mother and an Irish

Methodist father, and later married Wes McClung, the son of a Methodist minister and a Methodist suffragette. Her unrelenting faith inspired in her a sense of duty to her people, and she aligned herself with various Christian social activist organizations, through which she fought for women's rights and the rights of the underprivileged.

The Industrial Revolution, World War I, the Great Depression, and World War II are some of the powerful political and social events that provide a historical backdrop for Nellie's success as an author, activist, and social reformer. Throughout her life, she worked with and founded many organizations across the country, including the Women's Christian Temperance Union, the Canadian Women's Press Club, the Political Equality League, the Federated Women's Institutes of Canada, and the Canadian Authors Association.

Nellie contributed many other important achievements. In 1918, she was invited to speak at the Women's War Conference in Ottawa. In 1921, she was elected to go to London, England, to represent the Methodist Church of Canada at the Ecumenical Conference. In 1925, she launched an eleven-year-long campaign to have a female minister ordained in the United Church. And in 1938, she attended the League of Nations meeting in Geneva as the only Canadian female delegate.

With the help of her friends and supporters, loving husband and children, Nellie was an unstoppable force, carving a newer, brighter future for women and girls across the country. Nearly eighty years after achieving success for women in the Senate, her efforts have finally been properly acknowledged. In 2009, she and fellow members of the Famous Five, Henrietta Muir Edwards, Hon. Irene Parlby, Louise McKinney, and Emily Murphy, were posthumously appointed to the Senate.

Bibliography

Benham, Mary Lile. *Nellie McClung*. Toronto, ON: Fitzhenry & Whiteside Limited, 2000.

Davis, Marilyn, and Mary Hallett. *Firing the Heather: The Life and Times of Nellie McClung*. Calgary, AB: Fifth House Ltd, 1993.

Gray, Charlotte. *Nellie McClung*. Toronto, ON: Penguin Group (Canada), 2008.

Hancock, Carol L. *Nellie McClung: No Small Legacy*. Kelowna, BC: Northstone Publishing, 1996.

MacPherson, Margaret. *Nellie McClung: Voice for the Voiceless*. Montreal, QC: XYZ Publishing, 2003.

McCarthy, Tom. *Nellie McClung: The Girl Who Liked to Ask Questions*. Ottawa, ON: Novalis Press, 1985.

McClung, Nellie Letitia. *Nellie McClung, The Complete Autobiography: Clearing in the West and The Stream Runs Fast*. Toronto, ON: Broadview Press, 2003.

Millar, Nancy, and Frances Wright, ed. *The Famous 5: Nation Builders*. Calgary, AB: Famous 5 Foundation, 1999.

Savage, Candace. *Our Nell: A Scrapbook Biography of Nellie L. McClung*. Saskatoon, SK: Western Producer Prairie Books, 1979.

Wright, Helen K. *Nellie McClung and Women's Rights*. Toronto, ON: The Book Society of Canada, 1980.

Acknowledgments

Ontario Arts Council,
Writers' Reserve Program

Nellie L. McClung

Ray Cammaert

Shayla Dawson

Kalman Andrasofszky

Jukie Chan

Yessenia Rodriguez

Jonathan Barker

Ian Herring

Marcus Anthony To

Emily Pohl-Weary

Julia Pohl-Miranda

Irma Kniivila

Jenn Woodall

Samantha Haywood

Jennifer Notman

Caitlin Drake

Lynne Missen

Claudia Forgas

Chrystal Kocher

Sandra Tooze

And all the lovely people at Penguin Canada
and Transatlantic Literary Agency